This igloo book belongs to:

....

igloobooks

Published in 2019
by Igloo Books Ltd, Cottage Farm, Sywell, NN6 0BJ
www.igloobooks.com

Igloo Books is an imprint of Bonnier Books UK

1019 002
2 4 6 8 10 9 7 5 3
ISBN 978-1-78905-662-4

Written by Hannah Green
Illustrated by Sanja Rescek

Designed by Justine Ablett
Edited by Vicky Taylor

Printed and manufactured in China

Love you
more
igloobooks

I love you more than
jumping in rainy day puddles...

... or splashing in a bath all filled up with bubbles.

I love you more than swimming in the sparkly sea...

... or having an adventure
and climbing a tree.

I love you more than going on boats, planes and trains...

... or driving my racing car, zooming fast round the lanes.

I love you more than
ice cream on a hot, sunny day...

... or playing dress-up with friends
when they come round to play.

I love you more than
blowing out candles on a cake...

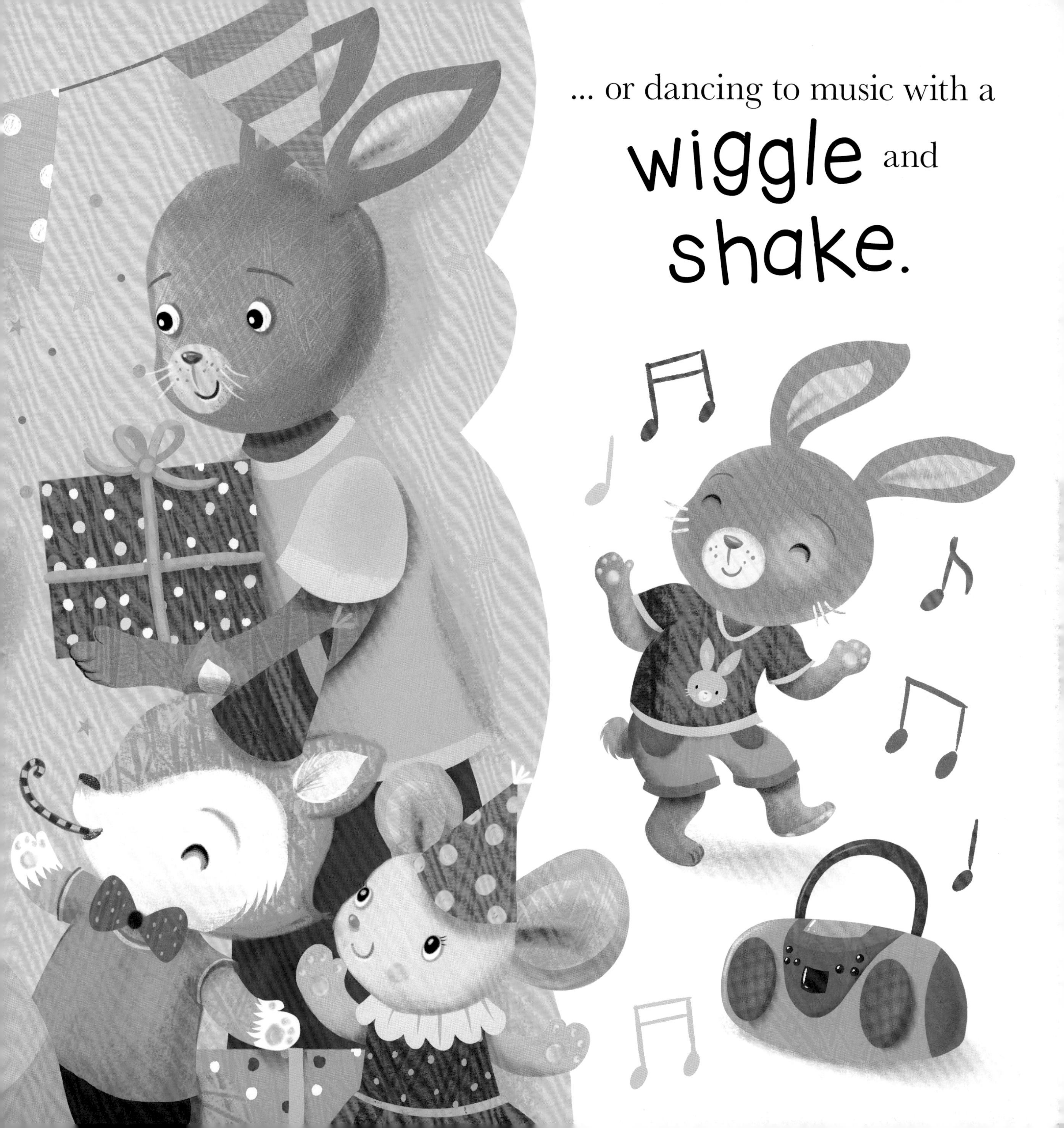

... or dancing to music with a

wiggle and

shake.

I love you more than choosing toys from the shop...

... or you **tickling** my tummy until I beg you to stop.

I love you more than eating
a freshly baked apple pie...

... or watching stars **twinkle** in the sparkly night sky.

I love you more than reading a book by the fire...

... or being pushed on the swings going higher and higher.

I love you more

than building snowmen
in the snow,
or sledging down hills
to see how fast we can go.

I love you more than any
of the things you do with me...

... because you are my fun,
caring, happy family.